LONG LOST

Writer
MATTHEW ERMAN

Art
LISA STERLE

Scout Production
KURT KNIPPEL

LONG LOST

Matthew ERMAN • Lisa STERLE

CHAPTER ONE

IN THE WOODS...

...AN OLD
GREAT BEAST
ROAMED...

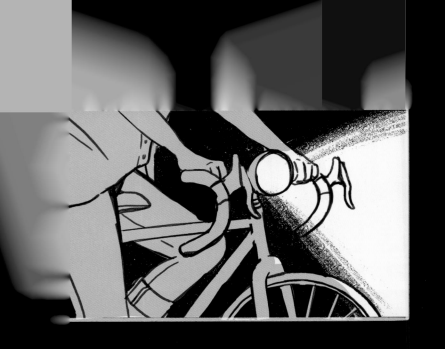

MOM'S BIRTHDAY IS SOON.

I HAVEN'T SEEN HER IN FIFTEEN YEARS.

WILSON RD

PART ONE
1
THE EXACT COLOR OF DOUBT

BEFORE LONG THAT MOMENT PASSES.

THE ONE I WAS WAITING FOR...

...AND I WAKE UP.

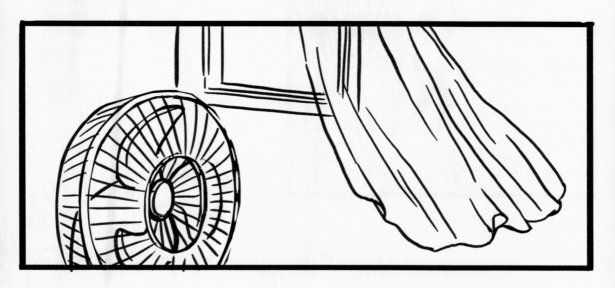

OKAY...UHHH
--POCKETS!
JUST STAY!
STAY THERE!
STAY!

UH...EWWW...

WHAT'S THIS
...WRAPPED
IN THE
HAIR?

TUG

CHAPTER TWO

THE OLD GREAT BEAST WAS MUDDING ITS TWISTED SNOUT...

THROUGH FORGOTTEN PASSAGES...

rustle

rustle

IN SEARCH OF SOMETHING...

FRANCES? OH— IT IS...IT IS YOU. BOTH HERE, HOW BLESSED.

Umm...

I COME TO— BRING YOU AN INVITATION...

HNG

HNG HNG.

DID YOU FIND POCKETS?!

TELL ME, WHERE IS HE?

PLEASE... PLEASE..I...NEED TO FIND HIM ...

OHHH... YOU'VE... GATHERED YOURSELF ONE OF THOSE BEASTS...

BOTHERING BEASTS HNH HAH HAH

YES, WELL. THIS IS FINE, THIS THING IS GOOD WITH I... IT IS SAFE.

I FOUND IT, YES. IN THE WOODS, SUCH A TERRIBLE PLACE. DO NOT WORRY. I AM IN...

DIRE NEED OF YOUR COMPANY... I, A MEAGER THRALL —OF CONCERN, YES...

IT IS — WORRIED BUT...SAFE, FED, WARM.

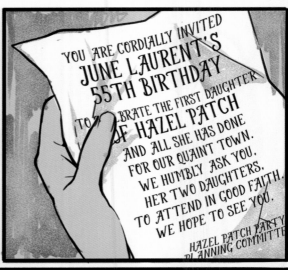

FRANCES! WHAT ARE YOU DOING?!

GIVE MY SISTER BACK HER DOG YOU THIEVING PIECE OF SHIT!

PL—PLEASE—I HAVE OVERSTAYED MY WELCOME...

AS I'M...WANT TO DO ...HNG HA.

HNG

HNG.

DO NOT WORRY,... I CAN BE AVAILABLE. YES, YES, AVAILABLE.

I WILL MAKE MYSELF AVAILABLE TO YOU, SOOOON.

THE COMMITTEE ANXIOUSLY...AWA--WAITS YOUR RESPONSE.

BUT... BEWARE THE WOODS WHEN YOU...

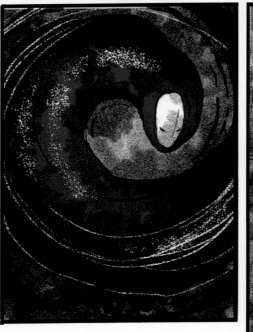

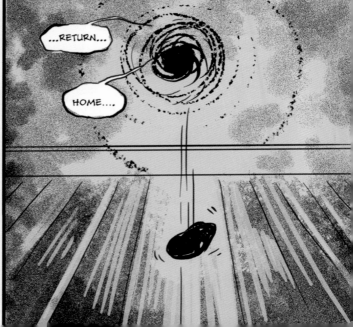

...RETURN...

HOME....

SO...IT'S BEEN NEARLY A DAY AND WE HAVEN'T SAID A WORD TO EACH OTHER....

WE DOING OKAY? YOU DOING OKAY?

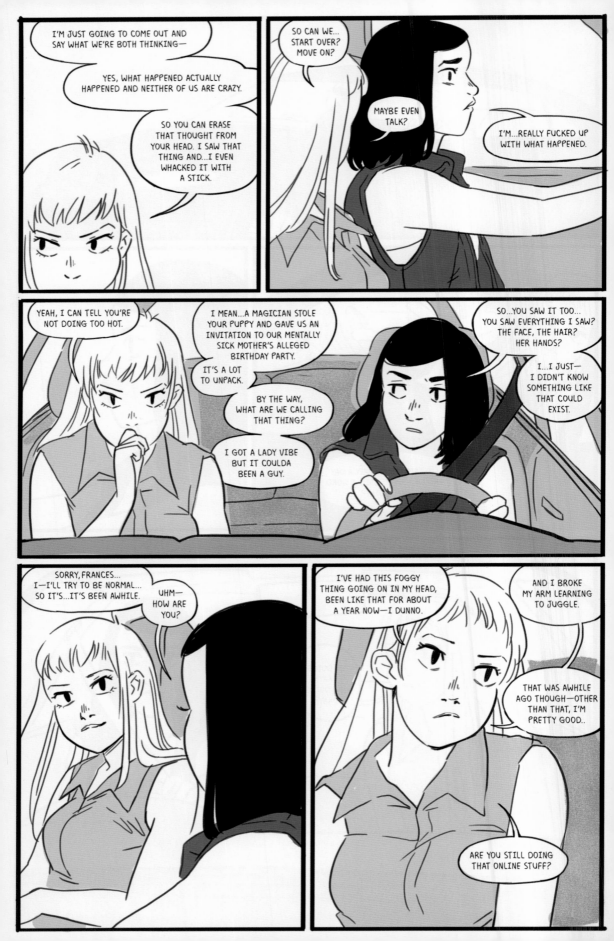

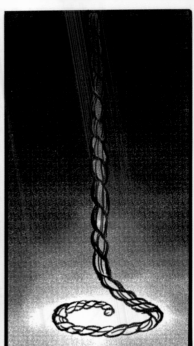

WIGGLE
WIGGLE

EVERYTHING OK
BACK THERE?

THIS KEY IS
GIVING ME SOME
PROBLEMS.

HOLD ON
A SEC.

GODDAMN
KEY WON'T
TURN...

JUST...TURN PLEASE...
JUST OPEN THE
TRUNK...
UGH!

PIECE OF
SHIT CAR.

ANOTHER THING
TO WORRY ABOUT
WITH EVERYTHING
...ANNOYING
SISTER...DUMB
CAR...HOME

OH MY GOD.

OH MY GOD!
PIPER! YOU HAVE
TO SEE THIS!

HUH?
WHERE'D
YOU GO?

Beware the woods
when you return home...

CHAPTER THREE

WHEN THE GREAT BEAST FOUND
NO FOOD, IT RESIGNED TO DIE.

To dream of that place is to dream betwixt two hills, under the gloam of that mountain.

In the recess of a holler... to dream of abandoned coal mines, to dream of vacant barns.

To dream of humans climbing onto frigid train cars and kicking their black stones off.

Their hands bloody and torn from the metal, their arms mangled...

...their throats and bodies full....

3 ELEPHANT WOMAN

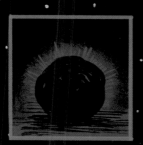

Do you dream of it?
The great gray...?

Was it you that
stood in the woods
drinking from that
deep hole...

...ripe with gore.
Or was it me?

Past my breath lay
dead...past the dead
lands lay a mountain...

...and is it you
who roots beneath?

CHAPTER
FOUR

CHAPTER FIVE

5 THE SHRINE

THE BEAST BOTHERED THOSE PRIMORDIAL THINGS FROM THEIR SLUMBER AND ASKED OF FOOD.

THIS IS ABSURD. I...I NEED SOME TIME.

WHO...WHO ARE YOU PEOPLE? YOU'RE STRANGERS.

I DON'T KNOW YOU. YOU DON'T KNOW ME.

MY SITUATION. MY SISTER. MY LIFE.

EITHER OF YOU. ALL THESE SECRETS... ALL MY LIFE.

YOU BROUGHT US HERE..AND I—I DON'T KNOW IF MY **FUCKING** MOM IS ALIVE OR DEAD.

WOW. COOL. A BRAND NEW AUNT. SAME AS THE OLD AUNT. DID I NEED A NEW ONE? THE OLD ONE WAS PRETTY BAD.

MAYBE NEW AUNT HAS MONEY...A GIANT INHERITANCE. SHE'S PRETTY. KINDA IMPRESSIVE CONSIDERING SHE LIVES IN THE WOODS...

MAN...I SHOULD LISTEN TO PIPER MORE OFTEN. SHE DIDN'T WANT TO COME.

WHY ARE WE HERE? I MEAN... I KEEP ASKING AND NO ONE CAN TELL ME.

AND YOU KNOW, PIPER COULD GET A NEW DOG.

IT'S NOT LIKE THAT ONE WAS ESPECIALLY IMPORTANT.

UGH...BUT NOW... MOM? IT'S LIKE ONE THING AFTER ANOTHER! I SWEAR TO GOD.

I WISH I HAD A DOG. I WISH I HAD A DOG RIGHT NOW.

MAYBE I SHOULD GO BACK AND TALK...FIGURE OUT WHAT TO DO NEXT...

TALKING TO YOURSELF?

YEAH, WELL...YOU HAVEN'T BEEN EXACTLY CHATTY LATELY.

DO YOU BLAME ME?

A LITTLE. WE'RE A TEAM AND RIGHT NOW I'M FEELING KIND OF AIMLESS. A LITTLE IN THE DARK ABOUT EVERYTHING AND YOU'RE NOT EXACTLY HELPING.

WHAT DO YOU EXPECT? I TRADED MY VAGUE EXISTENCE FOR THIS...NIGHTMARE. NOT EXACTLY THE DEAL OF THE CENTURY.

DID YOU HAVE A CHOICE?

DOES ANYONE?

SO...AUNT JOANNA.

YOU KNOW I CAN'T BELIEVE HER, ANY OF IT. IT'S ABSURD.

BUT SHE KNOWS MOM.

SO DO A LOT OF PEOPLE.

THERE'S NO REASON TO LIE, PIPER. IF JODY CORROBORATES IT, THEN YEAH — MOM HAS ANOTHER SISTER.

NOT THAT IT CHANGES ANYTHING. JOANNA WASN'T AROUND. SHE DIDN'T KNOW US OR TAKE CARE OF US. JUST ANOTHER STRANGER IN OUR LIVES.

IT WAS THEN THAT IT ALL LEFT.
WHATEVER IT WAS. THE AIR.
THE MOVEMENT.

WE HAD MOVED TO THE NAMELESS DYING RIVER. THIS IS WHAT THEY CALLED THIS PLACE.

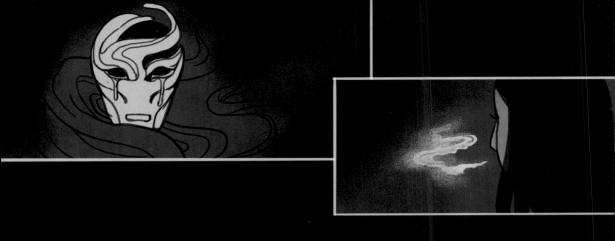

PIPER. FRANCES.

YOU MUST CROSS. Y-YOU MUST.

THIS...EXHUMED SPACE. WHATEVER LIGHT IT ONCE HAD, IS NOW GONE. WE LEFT THE WOODS OF HAZEL PATCH AND FOUND OURSELVES IN A PLACE NOWHERE.

BETWEEN MEMORY AND
HOME. BETWEEN THOUGHT
AND VOID.

IF YOU FIND YOUR WAY THROUGH THE WEEDS,
THE TURNING ROOTS AND DYING CROPS—
YOU'LL FIND YOURSELF HERE.

AT A FORGOTTEN PLACE. HAZEL PATCH.

CHAPTER SIX

BANG

PIPER! FRANCES! DON'T HURT EACH OTHER!

6 REVELATOR

"HOW MANY TIMES HAVE I GONE THERE NOW? I'VE LOST TRACK."
"I'M NOT GETTING ANY BETTER YET...I'M THINKING ANY DAY NOW."
"I'M NERVOUS BUT J. SAYS SHE KNOWS A WAY."

SCEEEEK
huff *huff*
SCREEE
grunt
THUD

HNNNGGG
HNNGNNGGG!
NO! WHAT ARE YOU DOIN—
SAVING US!
AAAAAAAAAHHHHHHH

Dear Reader,

Hello. My name is Matthew Erman and along with Lisa Sterle, we created this thing together. I'm going to be sappy for a moment because that is important to me (being sappy). Creating this book has been a highlight of my life, it's right up there with being married which, oddly enough, was also a joint effort between Lisa and I. We truly hope you've enjoyed our first six issues, the first segment to this two part series that I never dreamed would exist.

So let's talk about the book. If you're reading this letter before you've sat down and read the story, I'm excited for you. I think you're really going to like it and hopefully find something of yourself in either Piper or Frances (or maybe even Pockets). Lisa and I have poured our hearts and souls into this book, making sure it embodies what we love about comics, about genre and about the characters we've built. So thanks for picking this up, please enjoy.

If you're reading this after you just finished this, then I'll just go ahead and say; pretty crazy huh?! How good was all this, right? Lisa's art is so good, it's bonkers. I get it, you're in shocked silence. No worries, Lisa and I made sure you'd be pretty unhinged after issue #6. I betcha can't wait for Part 2, right?! Yeah, me neither. Anyway, thank you for reading this first bit and I hope it was good enough to get you hooked for the next bit, because that's it, our story is done and you've traveled a path with us. A dark path where things are not always what they seem, and in the center is a discovery about who you are, what you're meant to be, and how our relationships move us to be better people.

As a bonus, we have some prologue short comics that we commissioned our talented friends to make, as well as some incredible fan art.

Thank you for everything.
Matthew Erman & Lisa Sterle

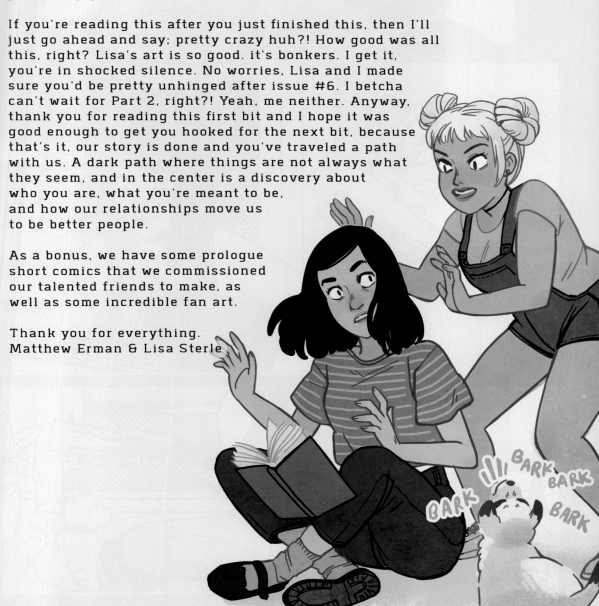

CREATED BY MATTHEW ERMAN & LISA STERLE / GUEST ARTWORK BY COLLEEN CLARK

YOU DOING OKAY, FRANCES? YOU JUST KIND OF... DISAPPEARED.

YEAH, JUST THOUGHT OF SOMETHING THAT SHOOK ME UP.

LYRICS FROM THE BAND INSIDE, I GUESS...

I DON'T KNOW, I'M FINE. I'M JUST BEING, LIKE, SUPER INTENSE.

YOU KNOW ME.

SUPER INTENSE.

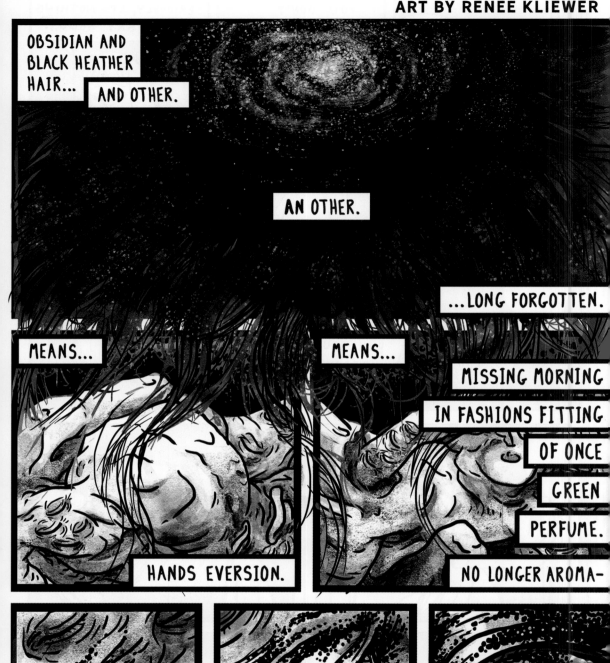

OBSIDIAN AND BLACK HEATHER HAIR...   AND OTHER.

AN OTHER.

...LONG FORGOTTEN.

MEANS...

MEANS...

MISSING MORNING

IN FASHIONS FITTING

OF ONCE

GREEN

PERFUME.

HANDS EVERSION.

NO LONGER AROMA-

I AM MYSELF...

...INSIDE OUT...

...ONCE AGAIN.

THIS BODY'S IN TROUBLE...

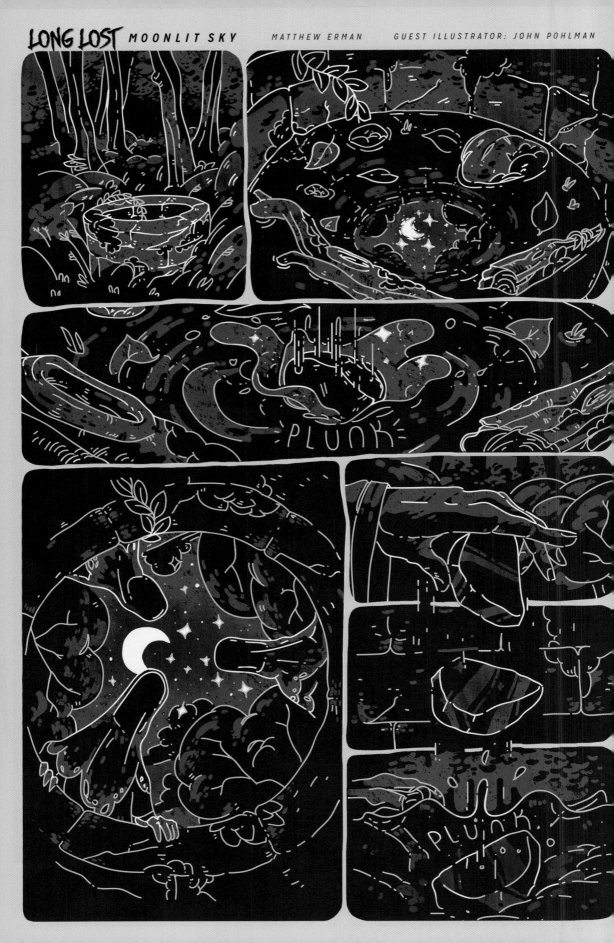